Mermaid Fu

Written by Lisa Thompson

Pictures by Craig Smith

"I can dive,"
said the mermaid.

"I can swim,"
said the mermaid.

"I can float,"

said the mermaid.

"I can dance,"
said the mermaid.

"I can jump,"
said the mermaid.

"I can hide,"
said the mermaid.

"I can play hide and seek,"
said the mermaid.

Think About!
What would be good about being a mermaid?
Who dances with the mermaid?
Who plays hide and seek?